NAUGHTY PUZZLE BOOK

Cheeky Brain-Teasers for Grown-Ups

Richard Cox

summersdale

NAUGHTY PUZZLE BOOK

An Hachette UK Company
www.hachette.co.uk

Summersdale Publishers Ltd
Part of Octopus Publishing Group Limited
Carmelite House
50 Victoria Embankment
LONDON
EC4Y 0DZ
UK

www.summersdale.com

Printed and bound by CPI Group (UK) Ltd, Croydon, CR0 4YY

ISBN: 978-1-80007-982-3

Substantial discounts on bulk quantities of Summersdale books are available to corporations, professional associations and other organizations. For details contact general enquiries: telephone: +44 (0) 1243 771107 or email: enquiries@summersdale.com.

INTRODUCTION

Whether it's sexting, talking dirty or humping your partner's brains out (or multi-tasking and doing all three!) we all have our ways of having naughty fun. But if you're looking for something to do in a rare moment when you're not working your way through the Kama Sutra, we might have the answer.

Raunchy riddles, arousing anagrams, sexy sudoku and climaxing crosswords all await the naughty of mind when enjoying some (not going) down time.

Some of the words and pictures you'll find – or have to draw in our daring dot-to-dots – might bring a blush to the cheek, so make sure this book is kept in the hands of adults only. The puzzles and trivia in here are definitely Not Safe For Work!

We hope you have fun with this puzzle book – and maybe you'll learn a thing or two along the way! Most importantly, remember you don't have to be fully clothed to enjoy it…

The first-ever push-up bra was invented in the USA in 1947 by Frederick Mellinger. What name was given to this bra?

a. The Over-The-Shoulder Boulder Holder
b. The Rising Star
c. Double Trouble

PAIRS

Can you match up the three sets of identical pairs?

NICKNAMES FOR BREASTS
WORD SEARCH

```
B N U Y R P O H M S X G H R P
Q Q J S W R T S N W Z Z J E N
T K G P C C U B R X E R H N P
A I V J C Z O Z D E S N O S A
W J T Y N O M L O C K H B G M
J Q B T B A D Y E W D C W U N
G O K S I S G A B N U F O J I
S X S O F E L Y R S B A W N Y
N E Z C L S S S R J A P B O K
R K I Q X Q X E G Y Z G U N T
U V B L E K T K Q R O I G J D
L C S L B O Y S P P N M H T N
N B D V O B N Y J G G E F G S
U J G H Z T U W F Y A I P G P
M E L O N S M J Y K S E T E R
```

KNOCKERS   MELONS   BOOBS

JUGS   TITTIES   FUNBAGS

HOOTERS   BAZONGAS   JUBBLIES

POSITIONS CROSSWORD

ACROSS

2 Ride 'em, cowboy! (7)

4 All in good faith (10)

6 Can be a bit of a mouthful (5,4)

DOWN

1 Spread your wings (9)

3 How much is that _____ in the window? (5)

5 No forking around (6)

WORD WHEEL

See how many words of three or more letters you can make, using each letter only once. Each word must use the central letter. Can you find the name of a common fantasy that uses all the letters?

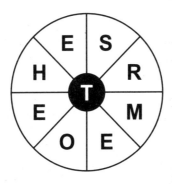

REBUS PUZZLE

Can you guess the two-word phrase based on the clue below?

Boobs

Boobs

Boobs

Boobs

WORD LADDER

Change NUTS into BALL by altering one letter at a time
to make a new word on each step of the ladder.

N U T S

— — — —

— — — —

— — — —

— — — —

B A L L

RAUNCHY RIDDLER

The answer to this riddle is something
you might do if you get to first base.

My first is in **FELLATE** and in **FEEL**
My second is in **ORGASM** and also in **MOAN**
My third is in **KNICKERS** but not in **PRICK**
My fourth is in **DICKS** but not **LICKS**
My fifth is in **LOVER** and also in **ORAL**
My sixth is in **CARESS** and also in **SQUEEZE**

What am I?

ANAGRAMS

Rearrange these letters to reveal four types of bras:

RID RUN WEED

GEL PUN

WREN DO

TOE BET CLAN

DOT-TO-DOT

Join the dots to find the mystery image!

REBUS PUZZLE

Can you guess the mystery word based on the clue below?

Skin

Skin

Skin

Skin

SEX TOY SUDOKU

Complete the following grid by filling in the empty
boxes with the missing icons. Each icon can
only appear once in a row, column or box.

MISSING WORDS

Fill in the blank space to make two compound words or phrases:

Hand		Done
Role		Book
Butt		Chain

COUNTING CONUNDRUM

+ = 14

+ = 17

+ = 13

= ?   = ?   = ?

TRACKWORD

Find as many words of three or more letters as you can by moving from one square to the next in any direction, without going through any letter square again. Can you find the naughty nine-letter word hidden in the square?

E	R	G
S	O	E
U	O	N

MAZE

Can you help find a path to make this Tinder hook-up happen?

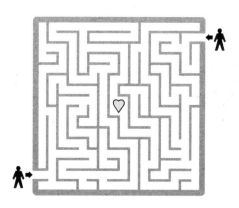

The "Orgasm Gap" shows that 95 per cent of straight men climax during sex, but it's a different figure for women. What is it?

a. 55 per cent
b. 65 per cent
c. 75 per cent

PAIRS

Can you match up the three sets of identical pairs?

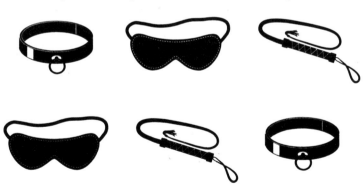

NICKNAMES FOR TESTICLES
WORD SEARCH

G	B	G	R	B	U	G	K	M	F	J	G	M	C	D
S	O	A	I	F	W	O	D	J	F	W	W	L	G	C
F	L	M	H	F	W	H	J	O	Z	J	A	V	S	O
G	L	L	W	R	U	B	E	T	E	B	O	D	Q	J
W	O	W	A	W	Q	S	G	W	Q	K	A	S	J	O
G	C	D	C	B	E	T	E	I	Y	N	S	Y	S	N
C	K	L	I	M	B	L	G	O	O	L	I	E	S	E
X	S	G	P	U	S	E	V	G	M	N	Y	A	T	S
W	H	B	F	M	M	F	R	T	K	U	C	W	Y	X
Q	O	B	O	V	Y	Y	S	R	D	I	N	E	Y	B
B	I	A	H	F	D	H	T	Q	I	R	J	X	S	L
M	X	W	H	T	A	K	U	C	L	E	M	H	E	Z
Q	X	Z	X	K	A	A	N	K	O	H	S	J	I	A
U	S	E	N	O	T	S	D	X	L	W	P	D	L	J
I	G	S	V	T	S	V	N	X	M	M	K	H	X	Q

BOLLOCKS	BALLS	GOOLIES
JEWELS	NUTS	BERRIES
STONES	GONADS	COJONES

COCK CROSSWORD

ACROSS

1 … of beef (5)

4 Also a helicopter (7)

6 Handy for checking your oil (8)

DOWN

2 Rhymes with roger (6)

3 Was British Prime Minister for a bit (7)

5 What an idiot (4)

**What are those suffering from
gymnophobia afraid of?**

a. Orgies
b. Veiny wangs
c. Nudity in general

BETWEEN THE LINES

What is the hidden word between the lines? The name of
someone who likes to lead you on can be written in the blank line
so that, reading downward, nine three-letter words are formed.

A	B	I	S	S	P	P	A	L
E	T	E	I	Y	N	P	S	G

ANAGRAMS

Rearrange these letters to reveal four
words and phrases for being naked.

UN ED

DRIP PEST

HET FUN BIF

THAT CHIT IS WOUT

WORD WHEEL

See how many words of three or more letters you can
make, using each letter only once. Each word must
use the central letter. Can you find the name of a
special type of performer that uses all the letters?

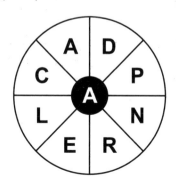

RAUNCHY RIDDLER

The answer to this riddle won't take long.

My first is in **QUEEN** and also in **QUEER**
My second is in **COUGAR** and also in **ROUGH**
My third is in **RIDE** but not in **RODE**
My fourth is in **CUCKOLD** but not **HOLD**
My fifth is in **KNOB** but not **BONER**
My sixth is in **QUIM** but not **MUFF**
My seventh is in **CREAM** and in **SCREW**

What am I?

WORD LADDER

Change BOOB into LICK by altering one letter at a
time to make a new word on each step of the ladder.

B O O B

— — — —

— — — —

— — — —

L I C K

DOT-TO-DOT

Join the dots to find the mystery image!

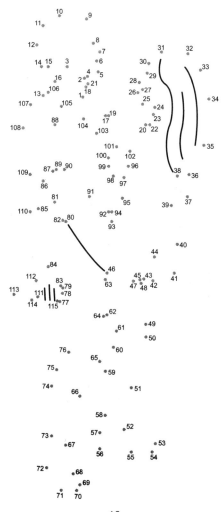

COUNTING CONUNDRUM

💋💋 + 💋💋 + 💋💋 = 48

(🎭🎭 x 💋💋) + 💋💋 = 240

👠 + (🎭 x 👠) = 32

👠👠 + (💋 x 🎭🎭) = ?

LINGERIE LINK UP

Can you match up each of the words on the left with one of the words on the right to make four longer words?

cor	suit
body	doll
strap	set
baby	less

TRACKWORD

Find as many words of three or more letters as you can by moving from one square to the next in any direction, without going through any letter square again. Can you find the naughty nine-letter word hidden in the square?

T	E	T
S	S	I
E	L	C

Which of the following was not a naughty 1970s sex comedy?

a. Adventures of a Taxi Driver
b. Adventures of a Plumber's Mate
c. Adventures of a Central Heating Installation Engineer

BUTT CROSSWORD

ACROSS

1 Rhymes with titter (7)
5 Old Blue Eyes this is not! (5, 3)
6 Never seen at a fun fair (9)

DOWN

2 Unlikely to be given when getting engaged (9)
3 She also (anagram) (7)
4 Unclean container (7)

WORD WHEEL

See how many words of three or more letters you can make, using each letter only once. Each word must use the central letter. Can you have a very hard think and find a word that uses all the letters?

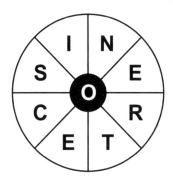

MISSING WORDS

Fill in the blank space to make two compound words or phrases:

Love		It
Head		Out
Give		Ache

23

ANAGRAMS

Rearrange these letters to reveal four
euphemisms for having sex:

O VAG LINK ME

GIN KNOB

LET GIN GIT DA

GREW NICS

REBUS PUZZLE

Can you guess the two-word phrase based on the clue below?

```
    L E G S
     L E G S
    L E G S
   L  E  G  S
```

SEX POSITIONS WORD SEARCH

```
P  B  Y  P  I  W  K  D  G  T  D  E  Z  H  L
I  M  U  Y  G  L  R  M  S  D  Y  M  T  E  R
L  S  F  T  C  B  O  E  B  N  I  C  N  H  I
E  R  L  R  T  D  B  H  F  S  O  I  B  G  G
D  Y  B  E  C  E  N  L  S  V  N  O  L  G  W
R  P  D  D  Y  B  R  I  D  Y  T  G  P  E  O
I  V  O  L  K  O  O  F  T  K  Z  K  A  S  C
V  B  G  E  K  N  U  X  L  N  W  N  H  V  E
E  G  G  U  A  U  I  V  A  Y  V  V  J  Y  S
R  U  Y  R  K  S  D  A  K  X  P  K  D  M  R
C  Q  Y  W  H  E  E  L  B  A  R  R  O  W  E
G  M  R  W  A  F  Q  Q  Q  X  S  U  A  K  V
Y  N  C  R  K  L  G  G  Z  P  N  A  Y  G  E
G  N  N  E  I  E  K  B  Q  H  F  G  R  O  R
L  R  I  G  W  O  C  D  D  J  W  T  A  A  P
```

DOGGY	SPOONS	WHEELBARROW
MISSIONARY	REVERSE COWGIRL	BUTTERFLY
COWGIRL		PILEDRIVER
	SIXTY-NINE	

MAZE

Can you help the Mistress find her Slave?

REBUS PUZZLE

Can you guess the three-word phrase based on the clue below?

BALLS

———

SHOW

FULL FIGURE CROSSWORD

ACROSS

1 Rhymes with lusty (5)
3 Beautifully constructed (4,4)
4 Also a type of cough (6)

DOWN

2 As in shelves (7)
4 Not a straight line in sight (5)

COUNTING CONUNDRUM

+ + = 15

(×) + = 35

+ (×) = 100

+ (×) = ?

MISSING VOWELS

Among the thousands of streets in Britain some rude names have ended up mounted on a road sign. Can you find the missing vowels in their filthy names?

M _ N G _   L _ N _

C _ C K   S T R _ _ T

G _ L D _ N   B _ T T S   R _ _ D

F _ N N Y   H _ N D S   L _ N _

B _ T T   H _ L _   R _ _ D

L _ _ S Y   B _ S H   L _ N _

B _ _ V _ R   C L _ S _

C R _ T C H   C R _ S C _ N T

"Morning Glory" is a term used to describe what?

a. An erection discovered on awakening
b. Pre-afternoon quickie
c. A sex position

PAIRS

Can you match up the three sets of identical pairs?

TRACKWORD

Find as many words of three or more letters as you can by moving from one square to the next in any direction, without going through any letter square again. Can you find the naughty nine-letter word hidden in the square?

B	R	Z
N	A	I
A	I	L

WORD LADDER

Change **BUTT** into **COCK** by altering one letter at a time to make a new word on each step of the ladder.

B U T T

— — — —

— — — —

— — — —

C O C K

BDSM WORD SEARCH

O	F	O	K	N	J	R	C	C	E	H	P	R	W	B
P	Q	Q	D	D	A	W	H	P	E	A	S	E	P	A
U	I	W	E	L	N	A	H	F	D	O	P	G	I	L
D	E	T	L	U	A	Q	R	D	G	S	W	G	Q	L
Y	J	O	N	I	P	B	L	M	M	K	J	O	U	G
H	C	R	T	I	O	E	L	N	X	X	M	L	D	A
D	O	U	Q	R	A	U	L	I	Y	S	V	F	X	G
F	P	G	R	Q	L	R	Y	V	N	C	P	V	M	T
H	S	Q	H	K	K	U	T	E	L	D	Y	T	U	I
C	Y	H	C	V	U	F	B	S	M	C	F	N	A	B
H	A	N	D	C	U	F	F	S	E	O	C	O	A	C
P	P	S	S	E	N	R	A	H	M	R	U	M	L	Z
L	T	F	A	R	E	J	N	W	A	A	R	O	D	D
S	L	A	H	E	C	W	B	D	N	J	X	B	V	Q
E	G	O	W	H	I	P	J	P	M	B	A	B	F	K

HANDCUFFS   PADDLE   FLOGGER

BLINDFOLD   HARNESS   COLLAR

BALLGAG   RESTRAINT   WHIP

ANAGRAMS

Rearrange these letters to reveal four sex toys:

RIVOT BRA

DO LID

ARS PONT

VOLE GEG

WORD LADDER

Change LUBE into TITS by altering one letter at a time to make a new word on each step of the ladder.

L U B E

— — — —

— — — —

— — — —

T I T S

ORAL SEX CROSSWORD

ACROSS

4 In Latin it's a bit of a mouthful (11)

DOWN

1 Meal for one (6,5)

2 Like you're in an elevator? (5,4,2)

3 Don't use a vacuum cleaner (7,3)

5 A generous gift (6,4)

RAUNCHY RIDDLER

The answer to this riddle is when two things are combined.

My first is in **ORGASM** and also in **MOANS**
My second is in **FELLATE** and also in **FELCH**
My third is in **EXCITE** but not in **ENTICE**
My fourth is in **ERECTION** but not **DICK**
My fifth is in **CLITORIS** and also in **RIDES**
My sixth is in **MELONS** but not in **HOOTERS**
My seventh is in **COMING** and also in **SCREWING**

What am I?

WORD LADDER

Change KNOB into SHAG by altering one letter at a time to make a new word on each step of the ladder.

K N O B

— — — —

— — — —

— — — —

— — — —

S H A G

MISSING WORDS

Fill in the blank space to make two compound words or phrases:

Trimmed		Fire
Shaven		Eating
Hairy		Deep

COUNTING CONUNDRUM

$$\text{(man kneeling)} + \text{(man kneeling behind)} = 13$$

$$\text{(man kneeling)} + \text{(person lying)} = 12$$

$$\text{(person lying)} + \text{(man kneeling behind)} = 11$$

$$\text{(man kneeling)} = ? \qquad \text{(man kneeling behind)} = ? \qquad \text{(person lying)} = ?$$

REBUS PUZZLE

Can you guess the two-word phrase based on the clue below?

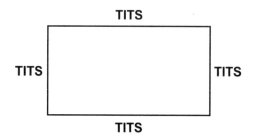

SEXTING SUDOKU

Complete the following grid by filling in the empty boxes with the missing icons. Each icon can only appear once in a row, column or box.

Every nationality is at it but according to a recent study by a condom-making company, the citizens of which lucky country are having it off the most?

a. Brazil
b. China
c. Greece

PAIRS

Can you match up the three sets of identical pairs?

WORD WHEEL

See how many words of three or more letters you can make, using each letter only once. Each word must use the central letter. Can you find the name of a messy end result that uses all the letters?

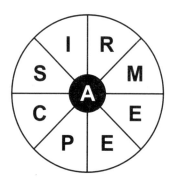

MISSING WORDS

Fill in the blank space to make two compound words or phrases:

Back		Man
Booty		Centre
Back		Way

RAUNCHY RIDDLER

The answer to this riddle will get you wet.

My first is in **SUCK** and also in **SPUNK**
My second is in **QUIM** but not **CUM**
My third is in **QUIM** and also in **CUM**
My fourth is in **TITS** and in **CLITS**
My fifth is in **ERECTION** but not in **COMING**
My sixth is in **FETISH** and in **SHAFT**
My seventh is in **JUICY** but not **JUGS**
My eighth is in **RANDY** and also in **RIDING**
My ninth is in **WANG** but not **WANK**

What am I?

ANAGRAMS

Can you rearrange the following to find ways of self-loving?

ABLE NICK FIT HENG

OK KENT HYMEN SAP

EHH BAP HIS BOTS

HE BE TAT MATE

MISSING VOWELS

Cocktails can be a great start to a night out. Some come with naughty names (though despite what you might think, the Harvey Wallbanger isn't one of them!) Can you find the missing vowels in these cocktails?

S L _ P P _ R Y   N _ P P L _

S _ X   _ N   T H _
B _ _ C H

B L _ _   J _ B

S _ X Y   M _ N K _ Y

W _ T   P _ S S Y

S _ X   _ N   M Y   F _ C _

_ N S   B _ R N _ R

T H _   L _ G
S P R _ _ D _ R

L _ C K   H _ R   R _ G H T

S _ X   _ N   T H _
D R _ V _ W _ Y

WORD LADDER

Change WHIP into CLIT by altering one letter at a time to make a new word on each step of the ladder.

W H I P

— — — —

— — — —

— — — —

C L I T

COUNTING CONUNDRUM

+ = 16

+ = 15

+ = 13

= ?   = ?   = ?

SEXY SUDOKU

Complete the following grid by filling in the empty boxes with the missing icons. Each icon can only appear once in a row, column or box.

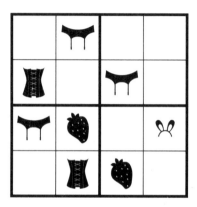

ANAGRAMS

Rearrange these letters to reveal four types of foreplay.

HAVE TETY PING

FINGE GRIN

DENSE CASBO

IK MAN GOUT

American actor and TV presenter Jonah Falcon has claimed to have the biggest cock in the world. How long is it when hard?

a. 25 cm (9.8 inches)
b. 29 cm (11.4 inches)
c. 34 cm (13.5 inches)

PAIRS

Can you match up the three sets of identical pairs?

FOREPLAY WORD SEARCH

```
S  G  N  I  Z  E  E  U  Q  S  L  I  U  I  N
J  U  F  G  S  I  J  Z  G  V  I  V  Y  V  J
X  Q  C  Y  N  Z  O  N  J  U  C  G  Q  R  W
N  S  T  K  W  I  I  V  V  B  K  R  V  H  D
P  J  T  H  I  L  N  R  K  E  I  I  S  H  L
I  B  Y  R  D  N  U  A  S  D  N  Z  M  Z  Z
M  H  Y  N  O  B  G  Y  O  R  G  F  H  G  H
X  X  O  M  B  K  N  J  Y  M  C  K  O  N  D
I  F  X  I  S  Y  I  W  D  K  O  K  B  I  B
P  S  N  B  H  Q  Y  N  X  S  E  L  D  S  M
C  G  Z  E  Q  S  L  Z  G  P  H  Q  R  S  L
H  N  U  F  A  V  Q  D  Q  R  U  I  S  E  D
R  O  S  T  I  Q  I  S  E  V  C  G  E  R  B
S  H  R  C  U  P  P  I  N  G  Y  Z  O  A  J
W  L  X  D  S  C  O  Y  Q  S  W  N  Q  C  J
```

SUCKING   SQUEEZING   FONDLING

LICKING   MOANING   CUPPING

RUBBING   CARESSING   STROKING

LOVE ROCKET CROSSWORD

ACROSS

4 Best launched under the waves – or sheets (4, 7)

5 Ham it up (4, 5)

6 Dance the night away on this (4, 4)

DOWN

1 Fires the cream (7, 8)

2 Available for filling up 24/7 (4, 4)

3 Best not to show it on the dancefloor (5, 5)

45

WORD WHEEL

See how many words of three or more letters you can make, using each letter only once. Each word must use the central letter. Can you find the name of a helpful substance that uses all the letters?

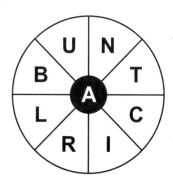

ANAGRAMS

Rearrange these letters to reveal four types of condoms:

DIBBER

O RUE COLD

LAUD OF REV

LICK NERF TERCH

MAZE

Which path should these lucky ladies
follow to get to the stripper?

Who or what is a "Lucky Pierre"?

a. A Parisian who gets a free lap dance
b. A Frenchman in a threesome with two women
c. A French euphemism for a condom

RAUNCHY RIDDLER

Nobody wants to know what theirs looks like in this two-word riddle.

First word
My first is in **COCK** and also in **CUCKOLD**
My second is in **FUCKING** and also **SUCKING**
My third is in **MELONS** but not in **SOLO**

Second word
My first is in **FISTING** and also in **FELLATIO**
My second is in **ANAL** and also in **LAID**
My third is in **LICK** but not in **KISS**
My fourth is in **JERK** and also in **TWERK**

What am I?

REBUS PUZZLE

Can you guess the two-word phrase based on the clue below?

ORGASM

ORGASM

orgasm

O R G A S M

Orgasm

ORGASM

orgasm

ORGASM

DOT-TO-DOT

Join the dots to find the mystery image!

MISSING WORDS

Fill in the blank space to make two compound words or phrases:

Butt		Team
Pussy		Out
Whacking		Limits

COUNTING CONUNDRUM

x = 72

x = 48

x = 54

= ? = ? = ?

TRACKWORD

Find as many words of three or more letters as you can by moving from one square to the next in any direction, without going through any letter square again. Can you find the naughty nine-letter word hidden in the square?

T	I	P
R	S	S
O	A	T

This well-known American lingerie company was founded in 1977. Is it:

a. Victoria's Secret
b. Victoria's Passion
c. Victoria's Pants Selling Company

PAIRS

Can you match up the three sets of identical pairs?

MISSING VOWELS

Porn movies sometimes take a little inspiration from books, TV shows and Hollywood movies. Can you name these porn parodies by finding the missing vowels?

_DW_RD P_N_SH_NDS

_ T_L_ _F TW_ T_TT__S

_V_RYB_DY D__S R_YM_ND

B_FFY TH_ V_MP_R_ L_Y_R

T_TS _ W_ND_RF_L L_F_

F_RR_ST H_MP

P_LP FR_CT__N

_NT_RC__RS_ W_TH _ V_MP_R_

R_M_NC_NG TH_ B_N_

SH_V_NG RY_N'S PR_V_T_S

MISSING WORDS

Fill in the blank space to make two compound words or phrases:

Circle		Off
Motor		Load
Rim		Offer

TRACKWORD

Find as many words of three or more letters as you can by moving from one square to the next in any direction, without going through any letter square again. Can you find the naughty nine-letter word hidden in the square?

S	C	H
A	O	I
M	T	S

WORD LADDER

Change TITS into COME by altering one letter at a time to make a new word on each step of the ladder.

T I T S

— — — —

— — — —

— — — —

— — — —

C O M E

ADULT WEBSITES WORD SEARCH

```
E N O V K P Z U B C B X I D Z
B I V J B K A J S U F J H G E
U M E V U X S C W E H D R Y P
T S V P T C V X X G L N I Y W
D A S O V X M I N C R A R W N
E J Y N S A Z A D O T M Z O P
R E G L R D B G P E Z T R L P
N V I Y S K F U L Q O G T V F
G I M F N Y O X H A M S T E R
G L O A H Y X P G U L E I N E
H N P N C U G Q Y U P U D D Y
F S C S E T A B R U T A H C U
H J H D S F V F P Z S B G L X
I X G C P Y K M Z F U T J B E
B H N W K E E K E S D H Y U C
```

PORNHUB	XHAMSTER	CHATURBATE
REDTUBE	XVIDEOS	LIVEJASMIN
YOUPORN	ONLYFANS	SPANKBANG

WORD WHEEL

See how many words of three or more letters you can make, using each letter only once. Each word must use the central letter. Can you find the name of a type of entertainment that uses all the letters?

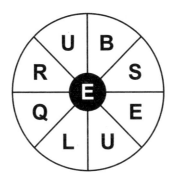

MAZE

Can you help Chloe find her skimpiest pants for her date later tonight?

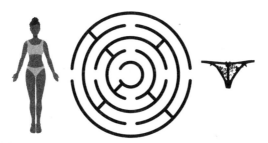

PAIRS

Can you match up the six sets of identical bottoms?

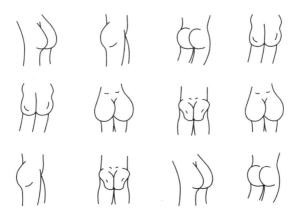

REBUS PUZZLE

Can you guess the mystery word based on the clue below?

DOT-TO-DOT

Join the dots to find the mystery image!

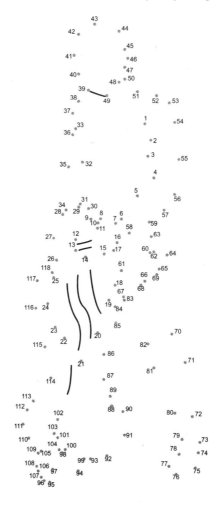

When you can't even wait to get to the bed, you may find yourself in a standing-up sex situation. But which of these is a euphemism for such a position?

a. Knee-trembler
b. Ass-freezer
c. Butt-chiller

PAIRS

Can you match the three burlesque dancers?

TRACKWORD

Find as many words of three or more letters as you can by moving from one square to the next in any direction, without going through any letter square again. Can you find the naughty nine-letter word hidden in the square?

G	N	I
C	A	G
O	T	T

COUNTING CONUNDRUM

+ = 22

x = 156

+ = 24

= ?   = ?   = ?

PAIRS

Can you match up the three sets of identical pairs?

WORD WHEEL

See how many words of three or more letters you can make, using each letter only once. Each word must use the central letter. Can you find the name of something that's useful for anonymous sex that uses all the letters?

DROP WORD

Can you find the word in the left-hand column that's made from the first letter of the seven answers across?

Across

1. This is done at the start, not on the golf course but in bed (8)
2. Get 'em off! (7)
3. Scares (anagram) (6)
4. Necking, snogging (7)
5. Not outside (6)
6. At the centre of things for the breast-minded (6)
7. PG Groin (anagram) (7)

LINGERIE WORD SEARCH

```
L  C  A  D  Y  G  P  K  R  T  V  E  C  C  S
R  S  I  D  R  D  E  F  U  C  L  R  X  H  G
U  S  K  H  R  V  E  O  V  B  O  O  H  T  N
D  R  I  Q  B  X  P  A  J  T  M  I  P  E  I
E  W  V  Q  G  G  H  I  C  N  J  M  M  Y  K
H  C  C  G  N  E  O  H  P  G  J  F  V  H  C
E  E  O  O  Q  Y  L  L  O  D  Y  B  A  B  O
M  U  H  R  A  E  E  D  R  V  F  X  L  H  T
T  T  Q  A  S  K  A  S  D  V  F  Z  L  J  S
M  H  A  S  J  E  T  T  E  N  O  C  L  A  B
T  J  P  Y  A  S  T  Q  K  Y  P  L  K  O  I
R  B  A  Z  S  B  J  H  W  I  W  S  Q  Q  Q
S  U  S  P  E  N  D  E  R  S  L  G  H  X  A
X  S  V  X  J  B  P  K  D  B  E  K  A  Z  I
W  N  T  S  Y  W  O  S  U  M  M  U  Y  X  Q
```

BABYDOLL	THONG	PEEPHOLE
BASQUE	SUSPENDERS	CROTCHLESS
STOCKINGS	CORSET	BALCONETTE

WORD LADDER

Change BLOW into FEEL by altering one letter at a time to make a new word on each step of the ladder.

B L O W

— — — —

— — — —

— — — —

F E E L

TRACKWORD

Find as many words of three or more letters as you can by moving from one square to the next in any direction, without going through any letter square again. Can you find the naughty nine-letter word hidden in the square?

R	I	S
U	O	M
E	Y	V

RAUNCHY RIDDLER

This two-word riddle will have you
focusing on the bigger picture.

First word
My first is in **HARD-ON** and in **HAND JOB**
My second is in **LICK** but not in **COCK**
My third is in **COMING** but not in **GROIN**
My fourth is in **NAKED** but not in **NUDE**

Second word
My first is in **NIPPLES** and also in **SLIPPERY**
My second is in **COWGIRL** but not in **DOGGY**
My third is in **CLAMPS** but not in **ANAL**
My fourth is in **SEXTING** and also in **SHAGGING**

What am I?

REBUS PUZZLE

Can you guess the four-word phrase based on the clue below?

MYCOMEMOUTH

VAGINA WORD SEARCH

```
M  G  R  M  M  V  G  M  V  Y  Q  K  F  K  N
A  O  U  Y  S  S  U  P  X  N  R  G  O  T  E
X  F  T  F  V  J  C  N  E  A  S  M  O  Y  D
F  O  Q  T  O  A  A  T  I  V  A  G  F  B  R
Q  G  T  V  O  F  J  J  W  Y  F  K  E  V  A
B  E  P  R  M  B  Z  A  D  I  U  Y  O  C  G
O  S  P  X  I  A  T  R  Y  D  M  O  A  G  Y
P  T  W  E  N  C  O  N  Z  J  P  T  A  Y  D
B  Z  V  U  G  W  O  D  O  A  A  A  B  U  A
C  E  H  H  E  Y  I  W  T  R  U  Y  U  W  L
I  E  A  P  W  J  N  D  N  Y  F  P  R  O  U
K  E  H  V  R  T  X  B  K  J  G  F  V  B  Y
C  N  A  A  E  V  H  Z  W  R  C  H  V  Q  Z
B  Q  R  N  Y  R  H  D  N  Z  T  W  R  Q  T
K  Z  W  W  L  G  L  J  B  J  E  Q  E  Z  L
```

BEAVER	PUSSY	VAG
MINGE	FRONT BOTTOM	VAJAYJAY
MUFF	LADY GARDEN	FOOF

65

CUM CROSSWORD

ACROSS

2 Go ned wart (anagram) (9)

4 This won't come out of any nipple (3, 4)

5 Add say duce (anagram) (5, 5)

DOWN

1 Not something you'd want in a pancake! (4, 6)

3 Possibly not found in a Xmas trifle? (3, 7)

6 Sounds like nick spruce (4, 5)

TRACKWORD

Find as many words of three or more letters as you can by moving from one square to the next in any direction, without going through any letter square again. Can you find the naughty nine-letter word hidden in the square?

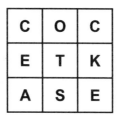

C	O	C
E	T	K
A	S	E

ANAGRAMS

Rearrange these letters to reveal
four slang terms for having sex.

YELL GOAT HAW

EG NOTING TIT

FIG NUCK

GUS BUM PILE

In the Swinging Sixties, a famous female singer was falsely accused of having what inside her at a party involving the Rolling Stones?

    a. Mars Bar
    b. Curly Wurly
    c. Creme Egg

WORD WHEEL

See how many words of three or more letters you can make, using each letter only once. Each word must use the central letter. Using all the letters, can you find a name given to someone useful with their tongue?

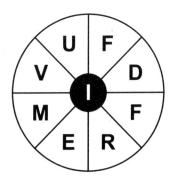

PAIRS

Can you match up the three sets of identical pairs?

MISSING WORDS

Fill in the blank space to make two compound words or phrases:

Cock		Head
Give		Fuck
Coming		Run

FANTASIES WORD SEARCH

```
P F M Z N I P D J U P T B F V
T E N S W B G V Y J J H G T A
G W G Y I N Z F P D M R N S E
S Z H G S R Z N F M C E I R Z
A P G Y I Z U Z O U Q E K O U
M E H L D N R E C F N S N L O
I J X F F P G K Y Y V O A E C
V S S U M A O K Y O G M P P O
X E S C I L B U P N V E S L B
H T X V D M G O I Q Z T L A D
K Y U I N Y Y G L S Z T A Y L
R X N C W Y N E Y E Q O G T Z
V G B L M I M S K N B W H I U
P R Z A W D O G G I N G N A O
Q N X S U U Z F Q F W A W U X
```

PEGGING	PUBLIC SEX	SWINGING
THREESOME	VOYEURISM	DOGGING
CUCKOLDING	SPANKING	ROLE PLAY

COUNTING CONUNDRUM

+ = 30

x = 396

+ = 37

= ?   = ?   = ?

MISSING WORDS

Fill in the blank space to make two compound words or phrases:

Front		Burp
Cock		Piece
Arse		Pipe

RAUNCHY RIDDLER

Take your time to find the answer to this riddle.

My first is in **FLAPS** but not in **PAPS**
My second is in **ORAL** but not in **ANAL**
My third is in **THRUSTING** and in **RECEIVING**
My fourth is in **BONER** and in **HOLES**
My fifth is in **SPUNK** but not in **KISSING**
My sixth is in **LICKING** but not in **SUCKING**
My seventh is in **RABBIT** and also in **VIBRATOR**
My eighth is in **WILLY** but not in **LEWD**

What am I?

**Scotsman Robert Burns once sang about
how "nine inches will please a lady".
What was he referring to?**

a. The size of a marrow he'd grown for his true love
b. The diameter of the dinner plate he served a meal on
during a date
c. The size of the penis guaranteed to provide satisfaction

NO STRINGS CROSSWORD

ACROSS

3 Laid lance (anagram) (9)

4 Don't have to dress up (6,3)

5 No subscription needed for a warm welcome (7,3,5)

DOWN

1 You can lie down if you want (3,5,5)

2 Phone sex? (5,4)

6 No hanging around (6)

Porn star Lisa Sparxxx holds the world record for having sex with the most men in one day. How many was it claimed to be?

a. 919
b. 879
c. 839

PAIRS

Can you match up the three sets of identical pairs?

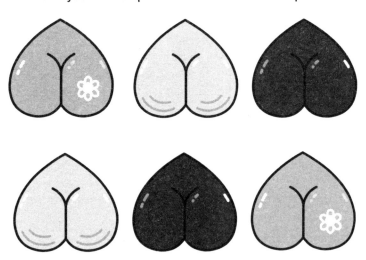

WORD WHEEL

See how many words of three or more letters you can make,
using each letter only once. Each word must use the central letter.
Can you find the name of a sex toy that uses all the letters?

REBUS PUZZLE

Can you guess the four-word phrase based on the clue below?

ANAGRAMS

Can you rearrange these letters to find four ways
of describing "dining in" with someone?

CHANCE GRUMP TIN

FAB SKI NET BREAD

A TINGE TO U

LAP GIN DRIVE

WORD LADDER

Change **HUMP** into **FUCK** by altering one letter at a
time to make a new word on each step of the ladder.

H U M P

— — — —

— — — —

— — — —

— — — —

— — — —

F U C K

RAUNCHY RIDDLER

The answer to this riddle describes someone
with an endowment that will attract interest.

My first is in **PRICK** but not **DICK**
My second is in **ASSHOLE** and also in **ANAL**
My third is in **COCK RING** and also in **SUCKING**
My fourth is in **KNOB** and also in **WANK**
My fifth is in **FINGERING** but not in **ROGERING**
My sixth is in **MINGE** and also in **GROIN**
My seventh is in **GRINDR** but not in **TINDER**

What am I?

**When spunk is ejaculated it can
reach how fast a speed?**

    a. 8 miles per hour
    b. 18 miles per hour
    c. 28 miles per hour

FIND THE WORD

Cross out all the letters that appear twice and then rearrange to find a word for getting it on.

P	I	H	M	H
A	N	L	T	O
O	U	Q	W	V
U	Q	D	R	Z
Y	D	G	K	A
C	F	K	L	P
X	J	V	S	J
B	T	Z	E	B
M	Y	F	X	F

COUNTING CONUNDRUM

REBUS PUZZLE

Can you guess the two-word phrase based on the clue below?

Which one of these terms is a euphemism for two singletons who have a very intimate relationship?

a. Friends with a range of sex toys
b. Friends with benefits
c. Friends with the Kama Sutra

TRACKWORD

Find as many words of three or more letters as you can by moving from one square to the next in any direction, without going through any letter square again. Can you find the naughty nine-letter word hidden in the square?

R	S	S
B	A	I
E	R	E

QUIM CROSSWORD

ACROSS

2 Sounds like thatch (6)

3 Blooms in spring (or any other time) (6)

5 What's new, _____ cat? (5)

DOWN

1 Cute and furry (6)

3 Further back in the USA (5)

4 Don't mess this up (4)

FETISH WORD SEARCH

```
N  J  U  P  D  X  B  R  C  Z  W  E  E  V  I
S  Y  T  F  N  X  E  I  I  A  Y  S  N  V  C
H  X  L  M  F  B  E  G  T  A  T  Y  E  K  V
R  P  V  O  B  K  S  E  A  N  V  W  M  C  C
K  O  L  U  N  V  R  X  I  D  P  Z  A  H  N
L  B  R  U  U  S  H  A  T  B  N  P  S  O  N
W  U  R  S  P  Q  R  S  S  J  N  O  W  S  X
D  E  U  O  I  T  J  G  U  M  D  P  B  E  K
K  J  R  X  S  S  C  N  R  N  J  K  Q  O  U
G  T  W  E  H  B  H  A  E  Z  E  C  X  H  W
S  M  R  P  G  S  C  C  A  F  B  B  A  S  X
L  E  A  T  H  E  R  J  W  Z  P  J  M  U  X
W  U  Q  J  B  S  G  O  X  Z  I  X  D  W  A
R  X  A  M  N  M  U  T  E  E  F  L  E  U  K
F  V  R  A  S  Z  C  U  Q  H  X  I  O  H  G
```

RUBBER	ENEMAS	BONDAGE
LEATHER	WATERSPORTS	SHOES
NYLONS	FEET	RESTRAINTS

WORD WHEEL

See how many words of three or more letters you can make, using each letter only once. Each word must use the central letter. Can you find the name of a very popular activity that uses all the letters?

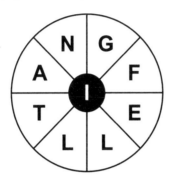

ANAGRAMS

Can you rearrange these letters to find four ways of describing a woman's private parts?

UNE VENT LOL

I RIPE HAY

FLIPS PASS

OH CO ICE

BETWEEN THE LINES

What is the hidden word between the lines?
A punishment for someone who's done something
naughty can be written in the blank line so that, reading
downward, eight three-letter words are formed.

A	A	P	E	S	T	A	E
S	T	P	D	I	T	D	O

RAUNCHY RIDDLER

The answer to this riddle can be a handful.

My first is in **BOOTY** and in **BUTTS**
My second is in **FONDLE** but not **FEELING**
My third is in **OGLE** and also in **LEG-OVER**
My fourth is in **BREASTS** but not in **TEASE**
My fifth is in **COWGIRL** but not in **CLUNGE**
My sixth is in **TOSSER** and also in **JERKING**
My seventh is in **SUCKING** but not in **FUCKING**

What am I?

**It is not easy to gain entry to The Mile High Club.
How do you become a member?**

a. Have sex up a Scottish mountain
b. Have sex while travelling in an aeroplane
c. Have sex on top of the Empire State building

PAIRS

Can you match up the three sets of identical pairs?

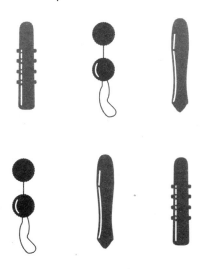

DOT-TO-DOT

Join the dots to find the mystery image!

RUDE PLACE NAMES WORD SEARCH

```
E  R  C  R  L  P  J  B  X  D  T  J  U  B  E
Y  W  H  D  S  H  J  S  E  T  X  F  M  J  O
E  Z  L  O  D  T  U  L  A  L  N  C  T  D  H
N  A  N  T  A  U  Q  W  P  C  L  L  Q  V  G
W  J  K  W  H  L  T  D  P  P  L  E  Z  M  N
H  U  P  P  E  R  D  I  C  K  E  R  N  D  I
L  F  G  S  H  I  T  T  E  R  T  O  N  D  R
E  M  S  W  K  C  P  F  S  K  V  J  L  V  G
Z  U  H  T  U  O  M  R  E  K  C  O  C  W  N
F  D  G  X  I  C  M  Y  U  L  W  E  E  Q  I
Z  G  S  B  J  K  O  O  E  X  T  T  O  C  F
D  L  H  O  D  S  B  P  A  Y  W  W  I  U  J
S  Y  Y  O  X  D  D  F  E  A  G  F  E  Q  K
Z  B  Z  A  Y  R  Z  L  N  Z  F  F  Z  L  O
N  A  W  J  N  C  O  G  P  C  E  R  Y  B  L
```

TWATT	COCKS	FINGRINGHOE
SHITTERTON	WETWANG	UPPER DICKER
BELL END	COCKERMOUTH	FELTWELL

NON-BED NOOKIE CROSSWORD

ACROSS

3 Handy for getting the head wet (6)

4 Get off while on this (5)

5 Oh butt (anagram) (3,3)

6 Get your bush trimmed here (6)

DOWN

1 Serving up something hot 'n' spicy on this (7,5)

2 Mile high, baby (5)

MISSING WORDS

Fill in the blank space to make two compound words or phrases:

Oral		Drive
Balls		Throat
Come		Drive

COUNTING CONUNDRUM

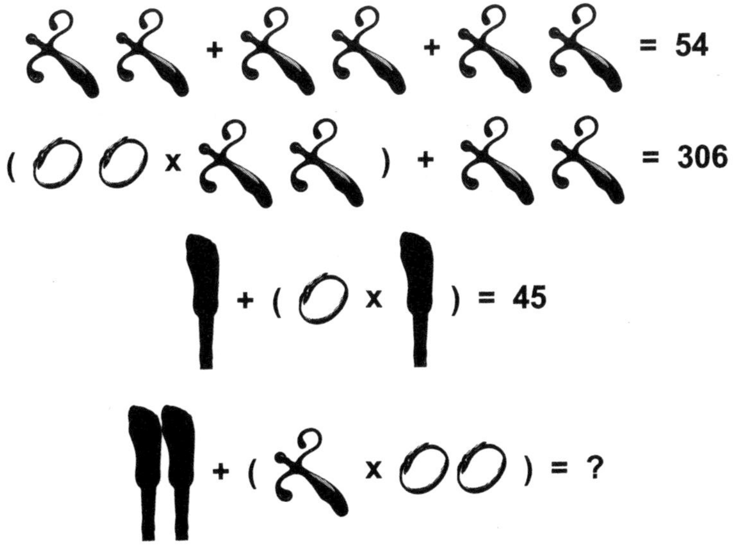

+ + = 54

(x) + = 306

+ (x) = 45

+ (x) = ?

Which part of the human body has the most nerve endings?

a. The penis
b. The testicles
c. The clitoris

REBUS PUZZLE

Can you guess the two-word phrase based on the clue below?

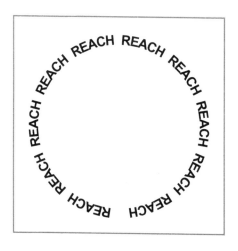

ANAGRAMS

Can you rearrange these letters to find four
euphemisms for being in the mood?

ON RHY

GIGOT GIN FRAG

THIN FROG

HOE BOTT RED HAND

WORD LADDER

Change **JOCK** into **BEAR** by altering one letter at a
time to make a new word on each step of the ladder.

J O C K

— — — —

— — — —

— — — —

— — — —

— — — —

B E A R

SCREW WITH MORE THAN TWO WORD SEARCH

```
Y  M  V  Z  Q  W  G  E  M  C  W  M  Q  E  S
D  A  I  S  Y  C  H  A  I  N  É  W  M  M  P
L  D  W  K  B  X  P  L  N  N  K  O  S  K  I
O  K  Q  E  P  D  Y  W  A  G  S  W  S  E  T
V  D  C  R  E  L  G  G  L  E  B  Z  Q  C  R
E  H  K  P  Z  R  E  W  E  G  O  A  F  U  O
W  T  K  Z  C  A  H  R  I  F  F  E  N  A  A
E  U  G  V  T  W  H  T  H  T  V  G  C  G  S
D  L  H  R  Y  T  N  A  Y  U  F  I  Q  G  T
G  S  O  H  C  N  U  M  D  N  A  P  M  U  P
E  I  M  E  A  T  A  N  D  T  W  O  V  A  G
S  C  P  F  I  F  J  X  G  O  W  S  W  P  I
S  C  G  C  J  H  E  Z  O  K  D  W  L  C  S
X  G  Q  I  S  V  X  E  X  Q  Y  N  Q  L  A
O  U  A  V  S  L  C  O  E  T  V  E  I  U  I
```

THREESOME	GANG BANG	THREEWAY
DAISY CHAIN	SPITROAST	MEAT AND TWO VAG
PUMP AND MUNCH	MÉNAGE A TROIS	LOVE WEDGE

92

PAIRS

Can you match up the three sets of identical pairs?

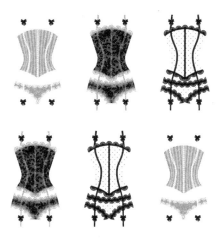

REBUS PUZZLE

Can you guess the four-word phrase based on the clue below?

CUM
—
MY TITS

**_Katoptronphilia_ describes
what sexual fascination?**

a. Licking eyeballs
b. Dressing up as a cat
c. Having sex in front of a mirror

WORD WHEEL

See how many words of three or more letters you
can make, using each letter only once. Each word
must use the central letter. Can you find the name
of a sexual position that uses all the letters?

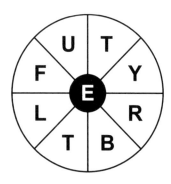

BETWEEN THE LINES

What is the hidden word between the lines? The name of a sex toy can be written in the blank line so that, reading downward, eight three-letter words are formed.

E	E	A	A	C	E	S	C
U	T	K	H	P	O	X	Y

COUNTING CONUNDRUM

+ = 15

+ = 20

+ = 17

= ?   = ?   = ?

MISSING WORDS

Fill in the blank space to make two compound words or phrases:

Well		Over
Wet		Job
Middle		Up

MAZE

Can you help Sienna find her way to her vibrator?

MISSING VOWELS

Britain is famous for its pubs. Some very naughty names end up swinging on the pub signs. Can you find the missing vowels in their names?

TH_ B _ _ V _ R

D _ R T Y D _ C K S

TH_ F _ M _ _ S C _ C K

H _ L _ _ N TH_ W _ L L

F _ L T H Y F _ N N Y'S

F _ N N Y _ N TH_ H _ L L

TH_ C _ C K _ N D S _ _ M _ N

TH_ B _ N G H _ L _

_ _ L Y J _ H N N _ _ S

TH_ P _ L _ S H _ D K N _ B

PUSSY STYLING WORD SEARCH

```
H  D  H  H  R  I  Y  G  T  B  O  X  Z  L  P
H  O  Z  S  S  Z  Y  G  B  R  C  V  A  S  O
D  B  L  R  U  W  Q  K  I  A  S  N  Q  W  S
H  Y  Z  L  C  B  E  F  T  Z  D  M  G  G  T
F  Y  L  F  Y  E  G  R  D  I  E  O  P  X  A
O  H  I  I  O  W  A  I  N  L  L  M  H  G
O  M  L  X  U  E  O  G  B  I  Z  O  Q  V  E
M  T  D  M  H  F  S  O  Q  A  Z  W  W  C  S
B  N  F  E  H  T  T  L  D  N  A  F  P  T  T
N  V  V  G  R  O  H  G  I  I  J  C  N  E  A
D  O  M  I  K  D  S  X  U  J  A  P  O  A  M
L  I  P  P  D  E  Z  W  A  C  V  R  K  B  P
E  L  G  N  A  I  R  T  A  D  U  M  R  E  B
L  G  P  Y  E  Q  P  O  A  R  R  O  W  B  I
G  C  Z  B  M  K  H  D  C  Z  C  T  M  P  N
```

HOLLYWOOD

BRAZILIAN

LANDING STRIP

BERMUDA
TRIANGLE

BIG BUSH

VAJAZZLE

LOVE HEART

ARROW

POSTAGE STAMP

ODD ONE OUT

Can you spot the odd one out?

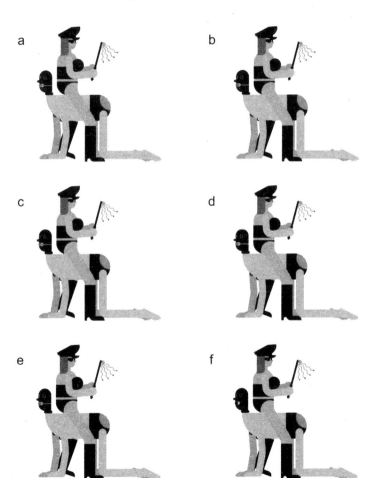

PAIRS

Can you match up the three sets of identical pairs?

WORD LADDER

Change PUBE into HORN by altering one letter at a
time to make a new word on each step of the ladder.

P U B E

— — — —

— — — —

— — — —

H O R N

SEXUAL ORIENTATION WORD SEARCH

```
C  S  I  F  S  T  L  K  J  P  P  W  H  Y  L
I  G  T  M  K  A  S  A  K  O  A  B  A  A  H
N  X  Q  R  S  F  C  J  U  D  N  G  U  W  F
R  Y  F  C  A  P  J  O  J  X  S  X  T  F  X
U  M  B  N  Q  I  Z  K  M  H  E  G  W  G  C
T  I  Z  E  T  R  G  J  Z  S  X  S  A  K  B
A  E  D  S  E  Z  B  H  O  A  U  P  I  V  Q
S  F  A  O  M  K  Z  R  T  N  A  G  Y  B  S
G  W  Y  G  U  H  D  E  C  K  L  M  C  T  A
Q  U  E  E  R  N  L  E  S  B  I  A  N  Q  Q
H  E  Z  R  A  M  P  V  X  E  F  M  H  O  C
O  T  L  J  V  G  Q  Z  H  K  C  I  J  C  F
U  N  C  I  T  N  A  M  O  R  I  N  M  O  P
Z  W  R  B  V  P  Y  X  G  V  D  N  V  V  N
J  H  W  U  B  D  P  B  C  G  P  U  A  D  T
```

ANDROSEXUAL	PANSEXUAL	SATURNIC
QUEER	OMNIROMANTIC	GAY
STRAIGHT	BISEXUAL	LESBIAN

FIND THE WORD

Cross out all the letters that appear twice and then rearrange to find someone who is not short in the trouser department.

M	L	H	N	B
A	M	A	U	E
K	F	K	X	T
W	X	F	D	Y
W	I	R	G	Q
Z	S	B	J	Z
T	C	U	P	I
P	E	O	V	Y
Q	J	V	R	D
Y				

REBUS PUZZLE

Can you guess the two-word phrase based on the clue below?

WORD LADDER

Change WANG into DICK by altering one letter at a time to make a new word on each step of the ladder.

W A N G

— — — —

— — — —

— — — —

— — — —

D I C K

ANAGRAMS

Can you rearrange these letters to find four sex toys?

PLAN LIMP PEC

CROC KING

SAME WAG SAND

PUB GLUTT

REBUS PUZZLE

Can you guess the mystery word based on the clue below?

$$\begin{array}{r} 3 \\ + 3 \\ \hline \\ \hline \end{array}$$

MISSING WORDS

Fill in the blank space to make two
compound words or phrases:

Heavy		Zoo
Making		Going
Feeling		Ward

**The world record for the distance when
ejaculating is held by Horst Schultz.
How far did his love juice go?**

a. 6 feet 9 inches (206 cm)
b. 9 feet 9 inches (297 cm)
c. 18 feet 9 inches (572 cm)

DOT-TO-DOT

Join the dots to find the mystery image!

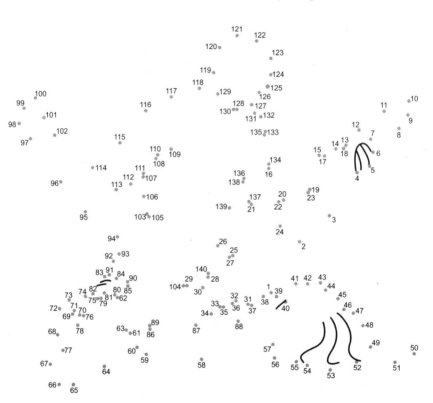

ODD ONE OUT

Which of the pants isn't part of a matching pair?

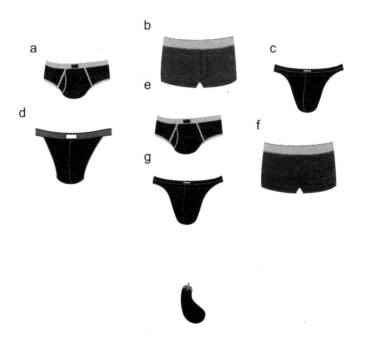

When a woman wakes up feeling horny, what is a euphemism for her state of lubrication?

a. Morning Dew
b. Morning Milk
c. Morning Juice

PAIRS

Can you match up the three sets of identical pairs?

WORD WHEEL

See how many words of three or more letters you can make, using each letter only once. Each word must use the central letter. Can you find another word for boobs that uses all the letters?

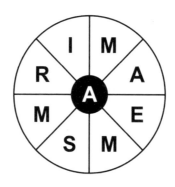

APHRODISIAC WORD SEARCH

```
C  S  U  H  I  C  N  N  M  N  J  X  I  S  E
H  E  H  Y  I  O  X  Q  S  I  C  I  E  J  B
O  I  V  K  V  Y  S  Q  W  I  C  I  O  X  J
C  L  L  S  I  W  E  F  L  I  R  Y  W  V  E
O  L  I  R  U  T  B  V  D  R  P  A  C  X  P
L  I  Y  E  K  U  U  L  E  V  T  Q  M  A  S
A  H  C  T  C  L  T  B  W  E  V  E  F  K  E
T  C  A  S  X  H  W  T  R  U  F  F  L  E  S
E  T  G  Y  V  A  A  M  G  S  L  D  W  J  E
Y  O  L  O  R  B  E  M  G  N  P  V  U  D  Z
J  H  L  T  G  L  R  I  P  V  E  Q  E  A  E
N  Z  S  A  O  S  F  M  M  A  X  S  I  Z  L
O  O  P  N  G  Q  K  K  S  Y  G  M  N  O  B
X  I  O  E  V  I  F  O  H  Q  I  N  V  I  H
P  R  A  Y  P  N  D  N  M  P  R  O  E  Y  G
```

OYSTERS	CHAMPAGNE	GINSENG
STRAWBERRIES	CHOCOLATE	HOT CHILLIES
TRUFFLES	WATERMELON	FIGS

How long it does it take sperm to swim the distance of 18 centimetres (7 inches)?

a. One minute
b. One hour
c. One day

TRACKWORD

Find as many words as you can by moving from one square to the next in any direction, without going through any letter square again. Can you find the naughty nine-letter word used in a bit of domination play hidden in the square?

T	N	I
R	E	A
S	T	R

ANSWERS

p.4 Trivia
b. The Rising Star

p.4 Pairs

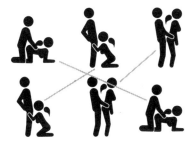

p.5 Nicknames for Breasts Word Search

p.6 Positions Crossword
Across: 2. COWGIRL,
4. MISSIONARY, 6. SIXTY-NINE
Down: 1. BUTTERFLY, 3. DOGGY,
5. SPOONS

p.7 Word Wheel
Word that uses all letters =
THREESOME

p.7 Rebus
Squeezed boobs

p.8 Word Ladder
One possible solution: NUTS,
PUTS, PATS, PALS, PALL, BALL

p.8 Raunchy Riddler
FONDLE

p.9 Anagrams
UNDERWIRED, PLUNGE,
WONDER, BALCONETTE

p.9 Dot-to-dot

p.10 Rebus
FORESKIN

p.10 Sex Toy Sudoku

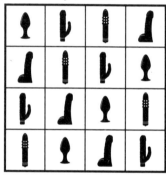

p.11 Missing Words
Hand (Job) Done, Role (Play)
Book, Butt (Plug) Chain

p.11 Counting Conundrum

p.12 Trackword
Nine-letter word: EROGENOUS

p.12 Maze

p.13 Trivia
b. 65 per cent

p.13 Pairs

p.14 Nicknames For Testicles Word Search

```
G B G R B U G K M F J G M C D
S O A I F W O D J F W W L G C
F L M H F W H J O Z J A V S O
G L L W R U B E T E B O D Q J
W O W A W Q S G W Q K A S J O
G C D C B E T E I Y N S Y S N
C K L I M B L G O O L I E S E
X S G P U S E V G M N Y A T S
W H B F M M F R T K U C W Y X
Q O B O V Y Y S R D I N E Y B
B I A H F D H T Q I R J X S L
M X W H T A K U C L E M H E Z
Q X Z X K A A N K O H S J I A
U S E N O T S D X L W P D L J
I G S V T S V N X M M K H X Q
```

112

p.15 Cock Crossword
Across: 1. Joint, 4. Chopper, 6. Dipstick.
Down: 2. Todger, 3. Johnson, 5. Dick

p.16 Trivia
c. Nudity in general

p.16 Between the Lines
COCKTEASE

p.17 Anagrams
NUDE, STRIPPED, IN THE BUFF, WITHOUT A STITCH

p.17 Word Wheel
Word that uses all letters = LAPDANCER

p.18 Raunchy Riddler
QUICKIE

p.18 Word Ladder
One possible solution: BOOB, BOOK, LOOK, LOCK, LICK

p.19 Dot-to-dot

p.20 Counting Conundrum

= 4, = 7, = 8
Sum: 8 + (8 x 14) = 120

p.20 Lingerie Link Up
Corset, Bodysuit, Strapless, Babydoll

p.21 Trackword
TESTICLES

p.21 Trivia
c. Adventures of a Central Heating Installation Engineer

p.22 Butt Crossword
Across: 1. SHITTER, 5. BROWN EYE, 6. POOPCHUTE
Down: 2. RINGPIECE, 3. ASSHOLE, 4. DIRTBOX

p.23 Word Wheel
Word that uses all letters =
ERECTIONS

p.23 Missing Words
Love (Handle) It, Head (Lights)
Out, Give (Head) Ache

p.24 Anagrams
MAKING LOVE, BONKING,
GETTING LAID, SCREWING

p.24 Rebus
Legs Spread

p.25 Sex Positions Word Search

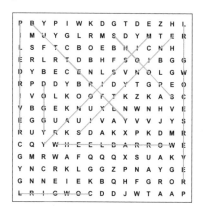

p.26 Maze

p.26 Rebus
Balls on show

p.27 Full Figure Crossword
Across: 1. BUSTY, 3. WELL-
MADE, 4. CHESTY
Down: 2. STACKED, 4. CURVY

p.28 Counting Conundrum

= 10, = 9,

 = 5,

Sum: 10 + (9 x 5) = 55

p.28 Missing Vowels
MINGE LANE, COCK STREET,
GOLDEN BUTTS ROAD, FANNY
HANDS LANE, BUTT HOLE
ROAD, LOUSY BUSH LANE,
BEAVER CLOSE, CROTCH
CRESCENT

p.29 Trivia
a. An erection discovered on awakening

p.29 Pairs
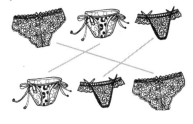

p.30 Trackword
BRAZILIAN

p.30 Word Ladder
One possible solution: BUTT, BUNT, BUNK, BONK, CONK, COCK

p.31 BDSM Word Search
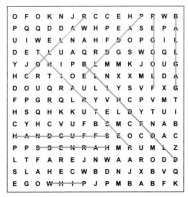

p.32 Anagrams
VIBRATOR, DILDO, STRAP-ON, LOVE EGG

p.32 Word Ladder
One possible solution: LUBE, TUBE, TUBS, TUTS, TITS

p.33 Oral Sex Crossword
Across: 4. CUNNILINGUS
Down: 1. EATING PUSSY,
2. GOING DOWN ON,
3. SUCKING OFF,
5. GIVING HEAD

p.34 Raunchy Riddler
SEXTING

p.34 Word Ladder
One possible solution: KNOB, SNOB, SNOG, SLOG, SLAG, SHAG

p.35 Missing Words
Trimmed (Bush) Fire, Shaven (Pussy) Eating, Hairy (Balls) Deep

p.35 Counting Conundrum

p.36 Rebus
Tits out

p.36 Sexting Sudoku

p.37 Trivia
c. Greece

p.37 Pairs

p.38 Word Wheel
Word that uses all letters =
CREAMPIES

p.38 Missing Words
Back (Door) Man, Booty (Call)
Centre, Back (Passage) Way

p.39 Raunchy Riddler
SQUIRTING

p.39 Anagrams
FLICKING THE BEAN, SPANK
THE MONKEY, BASH THE
BISHOP, BEAT THE MEAT

p.40 Missing Vowels
SLIPPERY NIPPLE, SEX ON
THE BEACH, BLUE JOB, SEXY
MONKEY, WET PUSSY, SEX ON
MY FACE, ANUS BURNER, THE
LEG SPREADER, LICK HER
RIGHT, SEX IN THE DRIVEWAY

p.41 Word Ladder
One possible solution: WHIP,
SHIP, SLIP, SLIT, CLIT

p. 41 Counting Conundrum

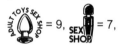 = 9, = 7,

 = 6

116

p.42 Sexy Sudoku

p.42 Anagrams
HEAVY PETTING, FINGERING,
SECOND BASE, MAKING OUT

p.43 Trivia
c. 34 cm (13.5 inches)

p.43 Pairs

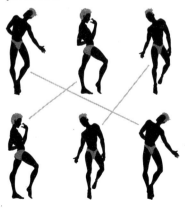

p.44 Foreplay
Word Search

p.45 Love Rocket Crossword
Across: 4. PINK TORPEDO,
5. PORK SWORD, 6. FUCK POLE
Down: 1. CUSTARD LAUNCHER,
2. LOVE PUMP, 3. DISCO STICK

p.46 Word Wheel
Word that uses all letters =
LUBRICANT

p.46 Anagrams
RIBBED, COLOURED,
FLAVOURED, FRENCH TICKLER

p.47 Maze
A

p.47 Trivia
b. A Frenchman in a threesome
with two women

p.48 Raunchy Riddler
CUM FACE

p.48 Rebus
Multiple orgasms

p.49 Dot-to-dot

p.49 Missing Words
Butt (Crack) Team, Pussy (Eating)
Out, Whacking (Off) Limits

p.50 Counting Conundrum

p.50 Trackword
SPITROAST

p.51 Trivia
a. Victoria's Secret

p.51 Pairs

p.52 Missing Vowels
EDWARD PENISHANDS, A TALE
OF TWO TITTIES, EVERYBODY
DOES RAYMOND, BUFFY
THE VAMPIRE LAYER, TITS A
WONDERFUL LIFE, FORREST
HUMP, PULP FRICTION,
INTERCOURSE WITH A
VAMPIRE, ROMANCING THE
BONE, SHAVING
RYAN'S PRIVATES

p.52 Missing Words
Circle (Jerk) Off, Motor (Boat)
Load, Rim (Job) Offer

p.53 Trackword
MASOCHIST

p.53 Word Ladder
One possible solution: TITS, TINS,
TONS, CONS, CONE, COME

p.54 Adult Websites
Word Search

p.55 Word Wheel
Word that uses all letters =
BURLESQUE

p.55 Maze

p.56 Pairs

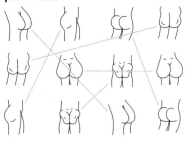

p.56 Rebus
Bukkake

p.57 Dot-to-dot

p.58 Trivia
a. Knee-trembler

p.58 Pairs

p.59 Trackword
COTTAGING

p.59 Counting Conundrum

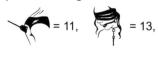

p.60 Pairs

p.60 Word Wheel
Word that uses all letters =
GLORY HOLE

p.61 Drop Word

1. Foreplay   2. Undress
3. Caress   4. Kissing
5. Inside   6. Nipple
7. Groping
Answer: Fucking

p.62 Lingerie
Word Search

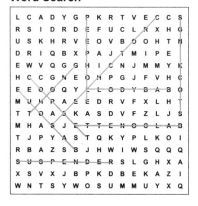

p.63 Word Ladder
One possible solution: BLOW,
FLOW, FLEW, FLED, FEED,
FEEL

p.63 Trackword
VOYEURISM

p.64 Raunchy Riddler
DICK PICS

p.64 Rebus
Come in my mouth

p.65 Vagina
Word Search

p.66 Cum Crossword
Across: 2. DONGWATER, 4. MAN MILK, 5. DADDY SAUCE
Down: 1. BABY BATTER, 3. NUT CUSTARD, 6. DICK JUICE

p.67 Trackword
COCKTEASE

p.67 Anagrams
GO ALL THE WAY, GETTING IT ON, FUCKING, BUMP UGLIES

p.68 Trivia
a. Mars Bar

p.68 Word Wheel
Word that uses all letters = MUFFDIVER

p.69 Pairs

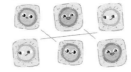

p.69 Missing Words
COCK (BLOCK) HEAD, GIVE (HEAD) FUCK, COMING (HOME) RUN

p.70 Fantasies
Word Search

p.71 Counting Conundrum

 = 15, = 22, = 18

p.71 Missing Words
Front (Bottom) Burp, Cock (Ring)
Piece, Arse (Crack) Pipe

p.72 Raunchy Riddler
FOREPLAY

p.72 Trivia
c. The size of the penis
guaranteed to provide satisfaction

p.73 No Strings Crossword
Across: 3. DALLIANCE,
4. CASUAL SEX, 5. NETFLIX
AND CHILL
Down: 1. ONE NIGHT STAND,
2. BOOTY CALL, 6. HOOKUP

p.74 Trivia
a. 919

p.74 Pairs

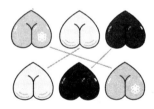

p.75 Word Wheel
Word that uses all letters =
COCKRINGS

p.75 Rebus
Bit on the side

p.76 Anagrams
CARPET MUNCHING,
BREAKFAST IN BED, EATING
OUT, PEARL DIVING

p.76 Word Ladder
One possible solution: HUMP,
BUMP, BURP, BURN, BURK,
BUCK, FUCK

p.77 Raunchy Riddler
PACKING

p.77 Trivia
c. 28 miles per hour

p.78 Find the Word
SCREWING

p.79 Counting Conundrum

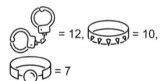 = 12, = 10,
= 7

p.79 Rebus
Cock ring

p.80 Trivia
b. Friends with benefits

p.80 Trackword
BRASSIERE

p.81 Quim Crossword

Across: 2. SNATCH, 3. FLOWER, 5. PUSSY

Down: 1. BEAVER, 3. FANNY, 4. MUFF

p.82 Fetish Word Search

p.83 Word Wheel

Word that uses all letters = FELLATING

p.83 Anagrams

LOVE TUNNEL, HAIRY PIE, PISS FLAPS, COOCHIE

p.84 Between the Lines

SPANKING

p.84 Raunchy Riddler

BOOBIES

p.85 Trivia

b. Have sex while travelling in an aeroplane

p.85 Pairs

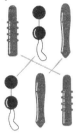

p.86 Dot-to-dot

p.87 Rude Place Names Word Search

p.88 Non-Bed Nookie Crossword
Across: 3. SHOWER, 4. TRAIN,
5. HOT TUB, 6. GARDEN
Down: 1. KITCHEN TABLE,
2. PLANE

p.89 Missing Words
Oral (Sex) Drive, Balls (Deep)
Throat, Come (Over) Drive

p.89 Counting Conundrum

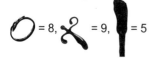

Sum: 10 + (9 x 16) = 154

p.90 Trivia
c. The clitoris

p.90 Rebus
Reach around

p.91 Anagrams
HORNY, GAGGING FOR
IT, FROTHING, HOT AND
BOTHERED

p.91 Word Ladder
One possible solution: JOCK,
JACK, BACK, BARK, BERK,
BEAK, BEAR

p.92 Screw With More Than Two Word Search

p.93 Pairs

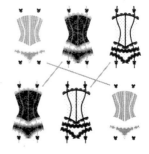

p.93 Rebus
Cum on my tits

p.94 Trivia
c. Having sex in front of a mirror

p.94 Word Wheel
Word that uses all letters =
BUTTERFLY

p.95 Between the Lines
MASSAGER

p.95 Counting Conundrum

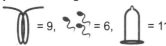

= 9, = 6, = 11

p.96 Missing Words
Well (Hung) Over, Wet (Dream)
Job, Middle (Leg) Up

p.96 Maze

p.97 Missing Vowels
THE BEAVER, DIRTY DICKS, THE
FAMOUS COCK, HOLE IN THE
WALL, FILTHY FANNY'S, FANNY
ON THE HILL, THE COCK AND
SEAMAN, THE BUNG HOLE, OILY
JOHNNIES, THE POLISHED KNOB

p.98 Pussy Styling Word Search

p.99 Odd One Out
f

p.100 Pairs

p.100 Word Ladder
One possible solution: PUBE,
PURE, PORE, PORN, HORN

p.101 Sexual Orientation Word Search

p.102 Find the Word
Schlong

p.103 Rebus
Reverse cowgirl

p.103 Word Ladder
One possible solution: WANG, WING, SING, SINK, SICK, DICK

p.104 Anagrams
NIPPLE CLAMP, COCK RING, MASSAGE WAND, BUTT PLUG

p.104 Rebus
Threesome (three sum)

p.105 Missing Words
Heavy (Petting) Zoo, Making (Out) Going, Feeling (Up) Ward

p.105 Trivia
c. 18 feet 9 inches (572 cm)

p.106 Dot-to-dot

p.107 Odd One Out
d

p.107 Trivia
a. Morning Dew

p.108 Pairs

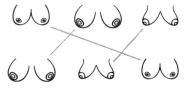

p.108 Word Wheel
Word that uses all letters = MAMMARIES

p.109 Aphrodisiac Word Search

p.110 Trivia

b. One hour

p.110 Trackword

RESTRAINT

Image Credits

Have you enjoyed this book? If so, find us
on Facebook at **Summersdale Publishers**, on
Twitter at **@Summersdale** and on Instagram
and TikTok at **@summersdalebooks** and get
in touch. We'd love to hear from you!

www.summersdale.com